Written by Tony Lynch
Edited by Melanie J Clayden
Designed by Joanna Davies

Published by Grandreams Ltd
Jadwin House
205-211 Kentish Town Road
London NW5 2JU

The condensed story in this annual is adapted from the original *Casper*
movie script.

Printed in Italy

CONTENTS

LEGEND HAS IT THAT THE HOUSE IS HAUNTED....

Who says there are no such things as ghosts? Just watch *Casper* the movie – take a look around Whipstaff Manor, in Maine, and you'll soon be convinced that ghosts really do exist!

Casper, a brilliant mix of live action and superb special effects, is the big screen hit of summer 1995 and will appeal to movie-goers of all ages.

The Official *Casper* Annual profiles the characters and the stars, takes you behind the scenes during the shooting of the film – and tells the exciting story of the movie.

Casper **is scary!**
Casper **is funny!**
Casper **is sad!**
Casper **is a spectre-filled spectacular!**

...FOR ONCE THE LEGEND IS TRUE!

Meet Casper...

Casper is the ghost of a 12-year-old boy. He is a friendly ghost, who likes real people and would love to play with real boys and girls.

Unfortunately, every time he tries to make contact with humans they always scream – very, very loudly – and he only succeeds in scaring them away! Like all self-respecting ghosts, Casper is able to 'morph' himself into practically any shape or object at all. He lives in Whipstaff Manor, along with his wicked uncles – Stretch, Stinkie and Fatso – known as The Ghostly Trio. They treat him badly and make him work as their slave. But Casper is ever hopeful that one day he will find a friend among the living. Then one day he meets Kat Harvey...

When Kat asks Casper what he's made of, he says, 'Well, you know that tingly feeling you get when your foot falls asleep? I think I'm made of that.'

Casper cleans up

-VOICE BOX-

Casper's voice is provided by 12-year-old actor Malachi Pearson. Executive Producer Steven Spielberg says, 'The voice of Casper, even more than his image, was the key, as it is the soul of the character.'

Director Brad Silberling agrees and says, 'Malachi is Casper as far as I'm concerned. He embodies the spirit of the character and has great charm, innocence and enthusiasm...and he's so endearing.'

However, it took three auditions before Malachi learned that he had won the part. 'When they called to say I'd got it, I just screamed!' he says.

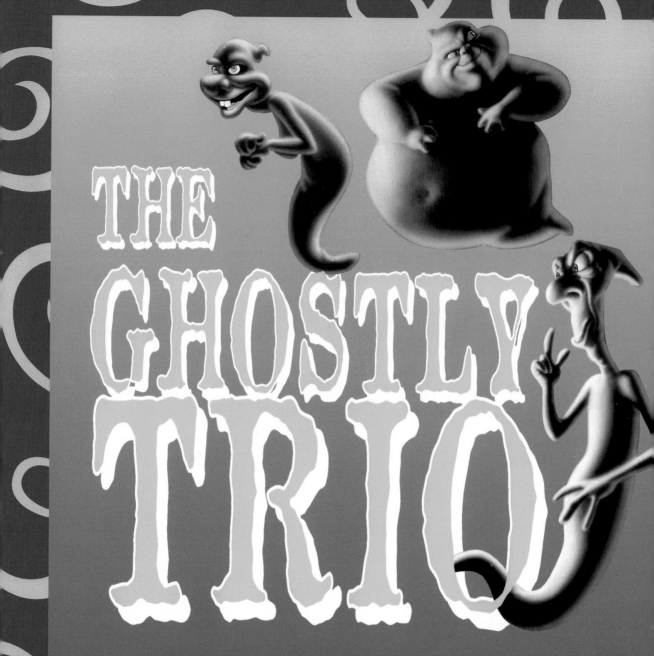

THE GHOSTLY TRIO

When Carrigan Crittenden inherits Whipstaff Manor, in Maine, she and her smarmy partner Dibs arrive there, intending to find its hidden 'treasure'.

This triggers the Ghostly Trio – Stretch, Fatso and Stinkie – into action. They do not want any humans, or 'fleshies', moving in on their territory. And they have successfully scared off all previous intruders.

They quickly get rid of a terrified priest brought in by Carrigan to exorcise the Manor. A 'ghostbuster' gets similar treatment – and even a gang of hard-hatted demolition men run out of the Manor screaming!

'Happens every time,' says Casper sadly. 'No-one ever wants to play.'

But the Ghostly Trio have a much tougher task in trying to frighten away 'afterlife therapist' Dr James Harvey, and his young daughter Kat. They try to intimidate them with a whole array of ghastly, ghoulish tricks...

Stretch

-VOICE BOX-

The producers auditioned many actors in the search for the right voices for the Ghostly Trio. These all-important roles were eventually won by three brilliant comic actors who were so funny during filming that crew members often had to stifle their laughter!

JOE NIPOTE, who brings Stretch to life, began on HBO's *Young Comedians Special,* which led to roles in various TV shows. He then became a popular radio personality in Michigan and later in California. Joe once did an impression of movie star Jack Nicholson, which even impressed Nicholson himself!

When the Ghostly Trio are hungry they open their mouths wide and shovel the food in – it falls straight through their bodies and splatters on the floor!

BRAD GARRETT, who provides Fatso's voice, stands 6' 7" tall. He is one of America's most popular funny-men, and was recently listed in the Top Ten Best New Comedians by the prestigious 'People' magazine.

Fatso

Stinkie

Stinkie's voice comes from JOE ALASKEY, an impressionist who was discovered by top voice artist Bill Scott. Joe took Scott's advice and moved to California – and was soon providing the voices for Plucky Duck in the Tiny Toon Adventures, Yosemite Sam in *Who Framed Roger Rabbit?* and The Lobster Mobster in *The Little Mermaid* TV series.

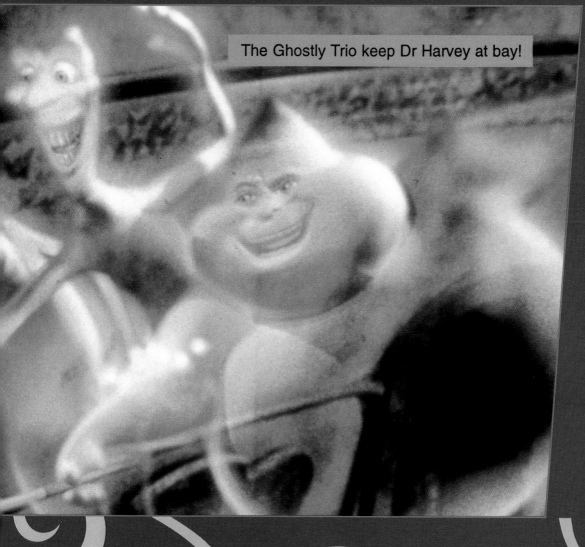

The Ghostly Trio keep Dr Harvey at bay!

Christina Ricci portrays Kat

MEET THE 'FLESHIES'

14

The central 'fleshie' role of Kat Harvey went to Christina Ricci who had previously enjoyed success as Wednesday Addams in *The Addams Family* and *The Addams Family Values*.
Christina has been acting since the tender age of eight when she started her career in TV commercials. She also appeared with Cher in *Mermaids* – and was seen in *The Hard Way* and *The Cemetery Club*.

CHRISTINA RICCI
as
Kathleen "Kat" Harvey

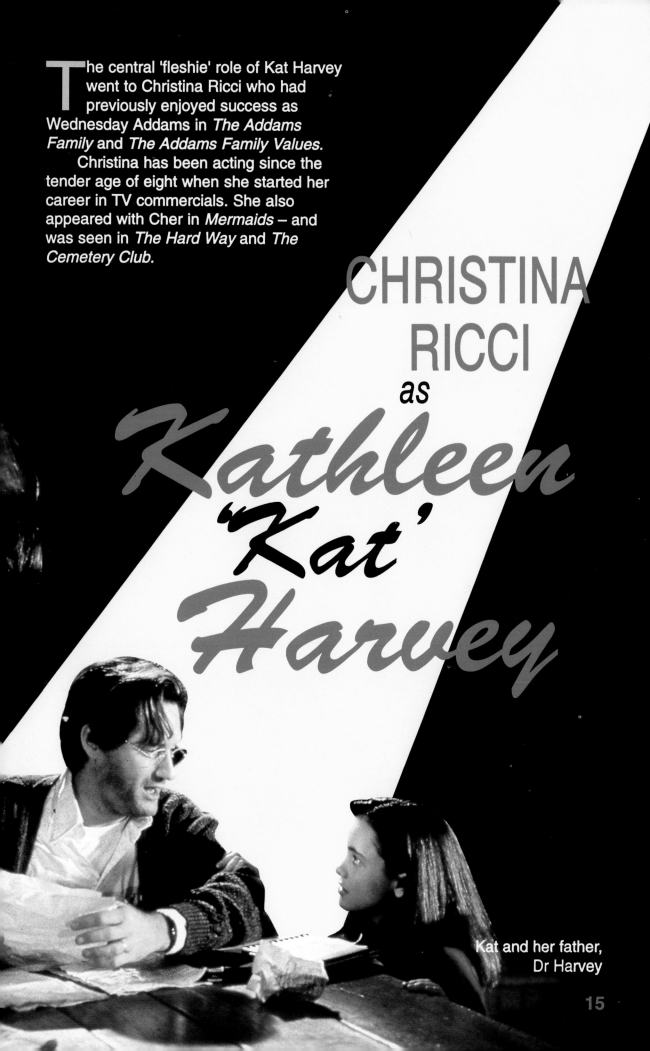

Kat and her father, Dr Harvey

Kat agrees to go to the party with Vic

On the very first day of shooting on the *Casper* set, Christina dispelled any doubts that director Brad Silberling might have had about her ability to act with characters invisible to her.

'I have a great imagination,' she told him. 'So I don't want you to worry about my seeing Casper and his uncles.'

'She was right,' says Brad. 'She has such a succinct imagination, she never had a problem – it was amazing how her imagination took over.'

Among the amazing things that Christina had to do in *Casper* was to take the fantastic rollercoaster ride on the 'Up-And-At-'Em' machine.

From its starting point in Whipstaff's library, and along its path to the underground laboratory, the contraption sprouted mechanical arms that washed her face, brushed her teeth, combed her hair and knotted a tie around her neck!

'The only annoying thing was that it kept going up and down and up and down...and fast,' says Christina.

Bill Pullman portrays
Dr James Harvey

Kat's father, Dr Harvey, is brilliantly portrayed by Bill Pullman. Bill has appeared in around twenty films since making his big screen debut in the 1986 comedy *Ruthless People*.

He first considered an acting career while studying building construction in New York. He switched courses and eventually gained qualifications in directing, from the University of Massachusetts. After teaching theatre studies at the University of Montana, he appeared in many plays in New York before moving west to California.

Bill is a chameleon-like actor with a wide range of brilliant characterisations to his name. In *Malice* he was the unsuspecting husband...In the smash-hit romantic comedy *Sleepless In Seattle*, he played Meg Ryan's allergy-prone fiancé...In *Spaceballs* he portrayed Captain Lone Starr. His other films appearances include *Wyatt Earp, The Accidental Tourist, Sommersby, Singles, Sibling Rivalry* and *A League Of Their Own*.

Casper director Brad Silberling wanted Bill to play Dr Harvey as soon as he heard him read the script. 'I never imagined anyone else in the part,' says Brad. 'It's a complex role – the character of Dr Harvey is the audience's eyes into the story and its anchor in reality.'

For Bill, the concept of acting with characters who are invisible took some getting used to. 'It was a very whimsical experience which required me to live in my imagination more,' he says.

Bill Pullman
as
Dr James Harvey

Dr Harvey and Kat are served breakfast by Casper

Carrigan and Dibs make plans

Cathy Moriarty realised she wanted to become an actor at the age of 14, when she first saw the romantic comedy *Born Yesterday* in her native New York.

Her big break came when she attended an open casting call where she met another aspiring actor. He encouraged her to send her photograph to a casting director who was looking for actresses for a film.

The actor was the now famous Joe Pesci and the casting director was casting for *Raging Bull*, the boxing biopic of the life of champ Jake La Motta.

Cathy subsequently won the role of Vicky, Jake's wife, playing opposite Robert De Niro – and she received an Academy Award nomination for her excellent performance.

Cathy Moriarty

as

Carrigan Crittenden

She later appeared in *Another Stakeout*, *Soapdish*, *Me And The Kid*, *Neighbors*, *Kindergarten Cop*, *The Gun In Betty Lou's Handbag*, *The Mambo Kings* and *Matinee*.

Cathy still shudders at the sheer physicality of the role of Carrigan Crittenden, which called for her to fall down steps...plummet off a cliff...stand very close to a huge swinging wrecking ball...and crash her car into a tree.

'But worst of all, they put me on a skateboard-type contraption that catapulted me down a hallway, whipping and spinning me around really, really fast while I was supposed to pretend to be kicking and screaming! I loved every minute of it,' she laughs.

Eric Idle portrays Dibs

British comedy actor Eric Idle provides many laughs as the sycophantic character, Dibs – and he forms a marvellous comic partnership with Cathy Moriarty who plays his bossy partner Carrigan Crittenden. Director Brad Silberling describes them as, 'The most wonderful and unlikely team you could ever expect to find, their rapport was immediate and astounding.'

Cathy says, 'I just loved working with Eric Idle. He is one of the funniest people I've ever met. We just had a blast working together.'

Indeed, people on the set were kept constantly entertained by the comic antics of the duo – on camera and off – and they were even told they ought to do a stint together at the famous Comedy Store!

Of course, Eric Idle has long been regarded as one of Britain's funniest actors – ever since his days with *Monty Python's Flying Circus*, the cult comedy series of the late-1960's.

Since then he has appeared in many movies including the Python's *Life Of Brian*, *The Adventures Of Baron Munchausen*, *Yellowbeard*, *Nuns On The Run* and *Splitting Heirs*. Eric is also president of the Prominent Features company which produced the brilliant comedy *A Fish Called Wanda*.

Eric Idle

as

Dibs looks worried.

WHIPSTAFF

The main action in *Casper* is set in the picturesque coastal town of Friendship, Maine. There stands a spooky, rundown house called Whipstaff Manor.

It's a fantastic old building that was once considered a fine home. Nowadays, it stands abandoned, desolate and broken down.

However, many of the good citizens of Friendship suspect that Whipstaff Manor might be haunted.

How right they are.

Let's take a look inside. Er...you go first!

What a spooky place! Dr Harvey explores Whipstaff Manor

MANOR, MAINE

The courtyard

Up in the attic

This is where the Ghostly Trio sleep

CASPER— BEHIND THE SCENES

'Casper' was originally created in the mid-1940s by Joe Oriolo who, together with Sy Reit, wrote a book about a young ghost who wants to make friends with humans.

The authors took the 'friendly ghost' concept and their unpublished book to Paramount Pictures. The idea met with a good reception and in 1945 the company released the first Casper cartoon, entitled 'The Friendly Ghost'.

The film did not catch on at first, but Paramount persisted with the concept and in the late 1940's two more Casper cartoons were produced. In 1949, Casper also made his debut in his own comic book. This time he met with great success – and a

television series followed a year later. In 1952 Harvey Comics took over publication of the Casper comic books and later acquired all rights for the character.

In 1989, Jeffrey A Montgomery acquired Harvey Comics and has reintroduced Casper to new and old generations alike.

Brad Silberling directs Bill Pullman and Christina Ricci

-SPIELBERG'S IDEA-

Steven Spielberg's idea to turn Casper into a movie production sprang from his memories of seeing and enjoying the cartoons in his own childhood. For the immense challenge of bringing Casper to the screen he called in director Brad Silberling and producer Colin Wilson.

Colin Wilson had previously worked on several productions for Spielberg's Amblin Entertainment, in editing and effects production. 'I believe his background on such films as *Who Framed Roger Rabbit? Jurassic Park* and *The Flintstones* uniquely qualified him for *Casper*,' says Spielberg.

Brad Silberling, a successful TV director, had almost worked with Steven Spielberg on a previous movie production, but the project had been abandoned.

'When *Casper* came up, I approached Brad about it,' says Spielberg. 'Although it was an ambitious film to hand to a first time director, I really felt with his ability and sensibility to do both comedy and drama that he was the best choice.'

Brad confesses to being a little surprised by Spielberg's initial approach. '*Casper* was to involve state-of-the-art computer effects, a large number of physical effects and an arduous post-production schedule,' he recalls. 'I asked him if he had called the right Brad!'

But Spielberg had great faith in Silberling, knowing he would have just the right attitude for the story.

Brad Silberling, Steven Spielberg and *Casper* crew members review a scene

'Wondrous imagination has gone into making *Casper*,' says Brad. 'Without offending anyone's memories of what Casper was, we've made him more engaging for today's audience. As we have created him, Casper has a real sense of humour and I think audiences are going to be surprised at where the humour leads.

-IT'S STATE-OF-THE-ART-

Turning the famous comic book character into a movie was a massive task requiring extraordinary collaboration between many different departments. Never before had such an intricate and extensive combination of live-action and state-of-the-art full-motion computer-generated images been attempted.

Screenwriters Sherri Stoner and Deanna Oliver did not limit themselves to thinking of *Casper* as either a live-action or animated film. Instead, they were given the freedom to imagine what a ghost could do that a human couldn't do. 'We never stopped to wonder whether anything we wrote could or could not be done on screen,' says Deanna.

Producer Colin Wilson then had to decide which of the scenes in the script would be physically realised and which would be produced as special effects.

'The basic framework of the movie is very reality based,' he says, 'but the ghosts go way outside the boundaries of the real world as we know it. We decided to use the technology that we developed for *Jurassic Park*, expand beyond it and take the next evolutionary step with computer graphics to create three dimensional character animated ghosts.'

-BUILDING WHIPSTAFF MANOR-

One of the first tasks for Production Designer Leslie Dilley, and his team, was to tackle the 'look' of Whipstaff Manor. They were determined to avoid the usual look of 'haunted houses' as seen in the movies. Inspired by the curving designs of renowned Spanish architect Antonio Gaudi they set to work creating a bizarre and beautiful 'Whipstaff' in which right-angles were obliterated.

Over 300 working drawings were made for the Manor's interior, exterior and grounds. The more elaborate sets,

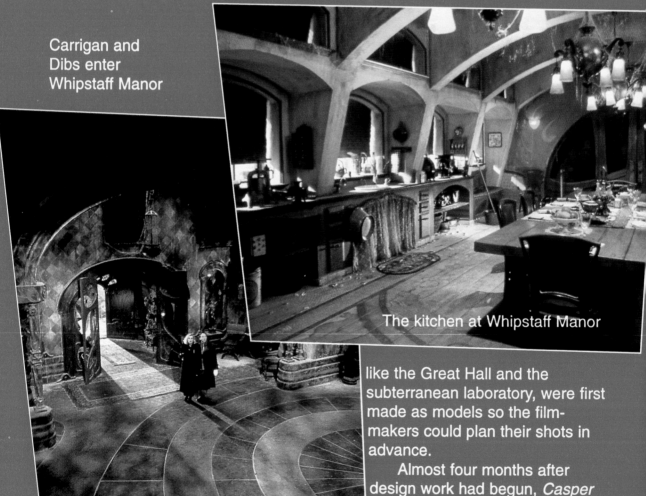

Carrigan and Dibs enter Whipstaff Manor

The kitchen at Whipstaff Manor

like the Great Hall and the subterranean laboratory, were first made as models so the film-makers could plan their shots in advance.

Almost four months after design work had begun, *Casper* encompassed three soundstages at Universal Studios, as well as

Kat in the magical toy room

space on the studio's famous backlot. 'The sets were incredibly complicated,' says Dilley. 'They housed special effects rigs, stunt mechanisms and lighting devices.'

When construction was completed, set decorator Rosemary Brandenburg and her crew began dressing the Manor. 'I wanted Whipstaff to relate to reality,' she says. 'I wanted a real sense that this was once a family's home – an unusual family's home headed by a wealthy, eccentric inventor. I tried to envision the choices they would have made for furniture, wall-coverings, tapestries, upholstery and carpeting.'

For the pivotal underground laboratory set, Brandenburg studied the lab of the famous inventor Thomas Edison and poured over turn-of-the century

scientific magazines for inspiration. 'I wanted everything that we put in the lab – machines, tools, and so on – to be based on real equipment.'

The final touch to the Whipstaff set was a fine layer of dust and a sprinkling of spider's webs, produced by 'hot-glue' guns. The finished effect was quite stunning. 'We were totally in awe of what was created,' says Colin Wilson. 'Whipstaff was quite exquisite and unique unto itself.'

Casper rustles up some breakfast

-GHOST-MAKERS-

Having worked on some of the most prestigious visual effects movies ever made, including *Who Framed Roger Rabbit?* and *Jurassic Park*, cinematographer Dean Cundey was not daunted by the demands and challenges of *Casper*. 'To me the most exciting film-making finds new ways to push the limits of film,' he says. 'Finding new ways to do things, adapting old ways to new ways – that's what interests me.'

For *Casper*, Cundey's challenges extended all the way from lighting the elaborate sets to capturing 'invisible' ghosts on celluloid. This was achieved in conjunction with the renowned Industrial Light & Magic (ILM) special effects company – and through the use of marvellous computer-generated ghosts and extra careful lighting of the real sets against which they would appear.

The faces of Malachi Pearson, Joe Nipote, Brad Garrett and Joe Alaskey – the actors providing the voices for Casper and The Ghostly Trio – were each videotaped while they read their lines. Their facial expressions and lip movements were

then incorporated into the computerised characters of the 'ghosts'.

Seven time Academy Award-winning special effects supervisor Dennis Muren also relished the challenge. 'We were interested in pushing the computer animation technology developed on *Jurassic Park* to the next benchmark, of convincingly animating a synthetic character,' he says. 'Compared to creating ghosts for *Casper*, the dinosaurs in *Jurassic Park* now seem rudimentary.'

Indeed, where ILM had to produce 52 shots for *Jurassic Park*, *Casper* needed around 300 – and they contain more complex effects than anything seen in the dinosaur epic.

The result is a masterpiece of computer-wizardry, allied to brilliant mechanical effects and marvellous acting performances.

Everyone who worked on *Casper* is immensely proud of the finished product.

What's on earth is that!?! Dr Harvey sees an apparition!

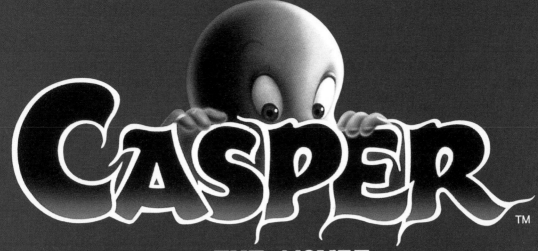

CASPER™

– THE MOVIE

Greedy Carrigan Crittenden is furious when she learns that her late father has left his vast fortune to a number of wildlife causes. 'To hell with the livestock - what did the old stiff leave me?' she asks Rugg, the lawyer who is reading the will.

'Uh, let's see,' he says, flicking through the pages. 'Dolphins... bobcats... owls...snakes...daughter Carrigan. Here you are - Whipstaff Manor in Friendship, Maine.'

'Are you telling me all I get is a lousy piece of property?' She snatches the deed of the house and tosses it into the fire.

As Dibs, her rather mousey partner, makes a grab for the deed, the heat brings out a hidden treasure map on one piece of paper. He strains to read it, '"Buccaneers and buried gold...Whipstaff doth a treasure hold".'

'Treasure!' yells Carrigan. 'Dibs, you idiot. Get it out. Get it out!'

But it's too late - the map turns to ashes.

'There's treasure in that house,' she says lustfully. 'Finally I'm going to get what I deserve.'

Carrigan and Dibs go to Whipstaff Manor, intent on finding the 'treasure' at all costs. But once inside the spooky old house they are alarmed by a disembodied voice.

'Show yourself,' orders Dibs.

Carrigan and Dibs await the outcome of the will

'If I do, don't scream, okay?' says the voice. 'I get that a lot.'

Casper, the ghost of a 12-year-old boy, materialises at the top of the stairs, slides down the banister and glides to a stop in mid-air - right next to Carrigan and Dibs.

Ouch! Dibs tries to snatch the treasure map from the flames

'No, no...' says Casper, as they open their mouths wide. 'You shouldn't do that. You'll wake the...' But they both scream as vapour swirls out of the floor and begins to materialise above the little ghost. They scream again, then escape to their car which gouges as gash across the lawn as they drive off at top speed.

Casper waves sadly. 'Come back anytime...Door's always open.'

Three large shadows loom over him. 'Just thought I'd warm them up a bit before I really scared 'em,' he says sheepishly, as a huge hand squeezes his neck.

Carrigan won't give up - not when 'treasure' is at stake. First she calls in a priest to exorcise the Manor...but he runs out ashen faced and wearing his head backwards! Another tries too, but is so scared he tells them to find someone else for the job! Finally they bring in a demolition crew - but the workmen stream out, shrieking, and drive their trucks away at top speed!

'Happens every time,' says Casper, sadly. 'No-one ever wants to play.'

That evening Casper floats around

A priest...

...a 'ghostbuster'...

...and a demolition crew - all fail to rid Whipstaff Manor of its ghostly residents

Friendship. In the Peters' house he sees Mr Peters watching a TV show about a certain Dr Harvey, a former psychiatrist who became an 'afterlife therapist' following the death of his wife Amelia - whose ghost he hopes to meet one day!

Casper watches with interest, especially when Dr Harvey's 12-year-old daughter, Kat, appears on the screen. He falls instantly in love with her and speaks her name aloud - which rather spooks Mr Peters!

Casper thinks up a plan to meet Kat. He enters the TV set and travels along the cable until he appears in Carrigan's hotel room. He moves her TV set close to her until she is gripped by what Dr Harvey is saying, '...I think we all know there are ghosts out there. I'm just trying to help people.'

Carrigan contacts Dr Harvey...

Kat shrivels at the news that she and her father are moving yet again. In two years she has been to nine different schools.

'I'll make you a deal,' says her father. 'Go with me this one last time. If I don't find what I'm looking for, then it's

Kat and Dr Harvey head for Friendship, Maine

over...No more "ghost mining".'

'You promise?'

'I promise.'

They drive to Whipstaff Manor, and are met by Carrigan and Dibs. 'We're desperate,' explains Carrigan. 'The house is infested and I'm at a complete loss.'

Dr Harvey reassures her, 'With time I'll help them move right on to the next plane.'

'What kind of time frame are we looking at?' asks Carrigan. 'Please tell me you just go in and spray the house.'

'A traditional psychological cure can take weeks, even years.'

'You didn't just say the word "years"?'

'It's conceivable.'

'No, no. No!' snaps Carrigan,

Kat and her father meet Carrigan and Dibs

losing her cool. 'Days is conceivable. Weeks, maybe. Months, no. Years, forget it!'

'It's her! She's here! She's in my house!' says Casper happily bouncing off the walls when Kat brings her baggage into Whipstaff Manor.

Kat is impressed by the creepy old manor. She finds a happy-looking bedroom and claims it as her own. In fact, it belongs to Casper. As Kat lays down, he 'morphs' into a pillow which she fluffs by punching him in the stomach, pummelling him and throwing him against the headboard!

He stands behind her as she unpacks, daring to make himself known. She tosses an old sock over her shoulder - right into his mouth. He spits it out - 'Blech!' Kat freezes at the sound and is horrified as he floats in front of her. She faints, comes round, then screams, 'Dad, I saw a ghost. A real ghost. A real live ghost!'

Dr Harvey bursts in. 'Ghosts can't hurt you,' he says. 'They're simply spirits with unfinished business. Okay?'

He checks in the closet and lets out a shriek of terror when Casper reveals himself. Dr Harvey throws Kat over his shoulder, runs down the stairs and hides her in another closet, before going off to investigate further.

Meanwhile, Casper's uncles, Stinkie, Stretch and Fatso - three odious ghosts determined to scare all humans away from Whipstaff Manor - return from a day at the races. 'Hey, Fatso,' says Stretch. 'You smell something?...Somebody's been living in our living room.'

'Somebody's been guesting in our guest room,' says Stinkie.

'Thank you for welcoming me,' says Dr Harvey, as three pairs of hidden eyes watch him. 'I would like to make contact with you.'

'Fleshies,' mutters Stretch.

Casper is delighted when he sees Kat

Next morning, in the kitchen, Kat is startled by Casper who wraps himself around her like a huge muffler. 'Pleasedon'tscream!Ipromiselwon'thurt youI'mafriendlyghost!,' he says quickly.

'If you scream, you'll wake up my uncles...I'm gonna let go now, okay?'
    Realising he really is friendly, Kat nods and Casper unwraps himself.
    'You're so cold,' she says.

Casper 'morphs' into a pillow for Kat   Kat - armed with a vacuum cleaner!

'I know - but it's great in the summer.'

'I can see right through you - what are you made of?'

'Well, you know that tingly feeling

Casper and Kat touch hands

you get when your foot falls asleep? I think I'm made of that.'

They reach out and their hands pass right through one another. 'Cool...' says Kat.

Kat trades insults with the ghostly uncles as she leaves for her new school, and Dr Harvey prepares for the

job in hand. 'Okay, guys. We obviously got off on the wrong foot here. I'll tell you what - let's meet in my office and start the process of crossing over. What do you say?'

This is what the Ghostly Trio think of Dr Harvey's idea!

The Ghostly Trio don't like this idea at all - and they pummel him with food!

As Dr Harvey attempts to counsel the Ghostly Trio, the conversation turns to his dead wife Amelia. They offer to put him in touch with her. 'Fatso, you know where Amelia floats. Go!' says Stretch.

'It's that easy?' asks Dr Harvey.

'We've got a ghost-to-ghost network,' says Stinkie.

Suddenly there's a knocking from inside a large closet. 'That is fast,' says Stretch. 'I...I think it's her.'

The door swings open and a female figure stands amid swirling smoke. 'Amelia?' says Dr Harvey.

The smoke recedes, revealing Fatso dressed as a woman. 'My man!' he says, smothering Dr Harvey with his big puckered lips, while Stinkie and Stretch howl with laughter at their latest cruel trick.

At school Kat is introduced to her new class-mates. A couple of kids heckle her as she tries to say 'hello' - and their shoe-laces become magically tied together beneath their desk!

She attempts to conceal her new address from the class, but eventually the truth comes out. 'Not Whipstaff?' says the teacher.

'Oh, you know it?' she says, guardedly. 'It's really kinda cool inside.'

One of the students suggests holding a Halloween party at Whipstaff. Everyone wants to see inside the spooky old manor, and Kat has to agree.

Kat is introduced to her new class-mates

In City Hall, Carrigan and Dibs study plans of Whipstaff Manor and discover an underground room containing an iron chamber shaped like a diving bell. '...I think we've found the treasure,' says Dibs.

At Whipstaff Manor Dr Harvey tries again to work with the Ghostly Trio, but they are as boisterous and disruptive as ever and advise him to 'Fughedaboutit!'

When Kat comes home, Casper admits he's acted like a total dork at school - so she lets him off the hook.

The Ghostly Trio - Fatso, Stretch and Stinkie

Dr Harvey lectures the spooks

Vic calls on Kat and asks her to go with him to the Halloween party. 'I'd love to,' she says.

Kat hums happily in her room, trying to decide how she'll wear her hair at the party. She opens a small jewellery box to find a tiny Casper dancing with the twirling ballerina inside. 'I'm a good dancer,' he says.

She opens a drawer and he is a folded shirt. In another drawer he becomes an unfurling 'ghost hooter' which hits her in the face. 'I'm always the life and soul of the party,' he says. 'Come on, we'd have a great time together.'

'Casper, I have a date.'

'What's that Vic guy got that I haven't?'

'A pulse?...A tan?...a reflection!'

'Okay, okay,' says Casper. 'But can he do this?' He morphs into a caped superhero, picks her up and flies her out the window and into a beautiful moonlit sky. They fly out to the lighthouse.

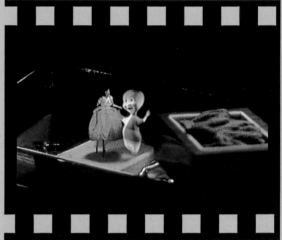
'I'm a good dancer,' says Casper

Kat asks him what he was like when he was alive, but he can't

Casper looks on when Vic calls on Kat

remember. In fact, he can't recall anything about his life.

'Is that bad?' he asks.

'No. Just sad,' replies Kat.

'I wonder why you don't remember anything?' says Kat, settling into her sleeping bag, back at Whipstaff Manor.

'When you're a ghost, your life doesn't matter much anymore. So you forget,' says Casper.

'Sometimes I'm scared I'm starting to forget my mom,' says Kat. 'The sound of her

Casper morphs into a shirt

voice...the way her fingertips felt when she'd run them through my hair...Casper, if my mom's a ghost, did she forget about me?'

'No, she would never forget about you.'

'Casper,' she mutters, falling asleep. 'Close the window, it's cold.'

He does as she asks, then crosses to Amelia's picture which stands by Kat's bed. He brushes it gently, then places his finger on Kat's forehead.

Amelia appears. Sitting on the edge of the bed she gently runs her fingers through Kat's hair, whispers in her ear and kisses her on the forehead. Kat smiles in her sleep.

Next day, Kat climbs up to the attic where she discovers a magical circular room piled high with boxes and toys. She opens the first box, and smiles.

Much to the annoyance of the Ghostly Trio, Dr Harvey begins packing up his belongings. 'Hey, Doc, you ain't thinking of packing it in now, are you?' asks Stretch.

'We was just starting to have fun,' says Fatso.

'It ain't often we meet a bonebag as amusing as you,' says Stinkie. But Dr Harvey keeps on packing.

'Time for dramatic measures,' say Stinkie.

' I think it's time we gave the Doc our own prescription,' says Stretch.

They swoop in and whisk Dr Harvey out the window.

Casper hears music coming from the attic. He floats up to investigate, following the sound to the toy room which is filled with light and alive with many moving antique toys. Kat smiles as he floats quizzically from toy to toy, inspecting each one closely. He floats up to a handprint hanging on the wall and places his hand on it. It fits. He floats over to a bookshelf.

'Now I remember,' he says. 'I used to stay up way past bedtime and read Treasure Island.' He takes a ride on a toy train, then he dives into a trunk and comes out wearing an ancient baseball cap - and holding up a beautiful antique lace dress. 'It was my mom's.'

'It's perfect,' says Kat. 'Do you mind if I wear it to the party...'

Kat tries on the dress

But Casper is lost in his memories, 'I begged my dad to get me a sled and he acted like I couldn't have one cos I didn't know how to ride it. And one morning I came down to breakfast and there it was. I went sledding all day, and my dad said, "That's enough". But I couldn't stop playing, I was having so much fun. It got late and it got cold and I got sick. And my dad got sad.'

'What's it like to die?' asks Kat.

'Like being born - only backwards. I didn't go where I was supposed to. I stayed behind so my dad wouldn't be lonely.'

Kat discovers an old newspaper and reads a story about Casper's dad claiming to be haunted by the ghost of his son - and that he had invented a machine to bring him back to life.

'The Lazarus,' confirms Casper. 'Wait til you see it.'

Unfortunately, this conversation has been overheard by Carrigan and Dibs, who have sneaked into the house to locate the 'treasure'. They follow Casper to

40

Kat rides on the 'Up and At 'Em' machine!

a secret balcony in the library, where he sits Kat in an overstuffed armchair.

'Hang on,' he says, tugging a crystal on a Tiffany lamp, which causes the chair to move. It travels along a track which leads down a long dark tunnel and through an 'assembly line' of robotic arms. 'Hands' reach out and slap shaving soap on Kat's face. She ducks to avoid being shaved by a razor. Then a towel wipes her face...Another automatic arm Brylcreems her hair and another combs it back. Then her teeth are

brushed, her shoes polished and a tie knotted around her neck.

'What was that!?!' she says, finally arriving in a subterranean lab built into the cliff beneath the Manor.

'My dad's "Up and At 'Em" machine,' replies Casper floating in through the ceiling. 'He was a great inventor, but he had trouble getting up in the morning.'

Back in the library Carrigan tugs at the crystal on the lamp and the chair returns to its starting point. She climbs aboard. Dibs is scooped into her lap and the chair makes its way through the tunnel once more. This time there's a malfunction and, before arriving in the lab, Dibs gets plastered from head to toe with toothpaste and shaving soap!

Casper reminisces in the lab. 'My dad and me played pirates, man we had so much fun. "Aye, matey. Buccaneers and buried gold, Whipstaff doth a treasure hold".'

Kat and Casper search for the Lazarus machine, but without much luck until Kat opens a dusty old copy of Frankenstein. The book is the switch which causes a spherical chamber to rise in a pool in the centre of the lab. Steel steps glide along a track to meet the chamber, the vacuum seal on the

Dibs comes off worse on board the 'Up and At 'Em' machine

door opens. 'Lazarus,' says Casper.

'This was supposed to bring you back to life?'

'My dad got sent away before he could use it on me.'

The Lazarus!

They find a capsule full of red liquid. 'Careful,' says Casper. 'That's what brings ghosts back to life. There's just enough for one.'

He gazes thoughtfully at the capsule, then with conviction places it in a slot in the machine and enters the chamber. 'Press the button,' he says. 'I'm gonna be alive.'

Kat is amazed at the importance of the decision he has made, but just as she locates the start button, Carrigan's hand reaches in and grabs the capsule. The Lazarus splutters and stalls and Casper is left flopping about inside - still a blue-eyed blob.

The Ghostly Trio have taken Dr Harvey to the High Spirits bar. He sings along to a karaoke machine - even the ghosts can't stand it. 'We gotta get back Doc,' says Stinkie.

But he breaks into another song.

The Trio have discovered that they genuinely like him. 'He's sure got a lot

of spirit,' says Stretch.

'Yeah, but the poor guy's still got his whole miserable life ahead of him,' adds Stinkie.

'We could do him a favour,' says Fatso. '...put him out of his misery.'

'Yeah. We've been the Ghostly Trio for long enough. Time to make it a quartet,' says Stretch.

In order to do their new friend a 'favour' they creep up on him with a shotgun, a broken bottle and a fishing spear, as he sings a rock number. But his foot nudges the karaoke machine and the record changes to a slow, heartbreaking ballad - so moving that the ghosts can't do the dirty deed.

Unaware of their weapons, Dr Harvey tells them just how much Kat means to him and how sorry he is to drag her around the country. 'She hasn't been able to form any ties, to makes any friends. But you know what, neither have I...until now! You guys remind me of what it's like to hang out with the boys. To share the good times...I don't feel alone...I love you guys.'

The ghosts start to weep and drop

their weapons. 'I can't croak him,' says Fatso.

'Me neither...no way,' says Stretch.

'The night's young boys,' says Dr

Casper prepares to enter the Lazarus

Harvey. 'We're clearing out every bar this town's got. Let's move.' He marches out of the door and falls with a horrible thud into an open trench in the street!

Carrigan clutches the capsule. 'Do you know what this means? No more fear of death. One minute you're a ghost, free to come and go as you please, the next you're back on your feet.'

Dibs joins in. 'You could fly through...'

'...walls,' says Carrigan, 'thick walls. Get to whatever's behind those walls...'

'...Treasure for example...'

'...Then pop back to life again and head for the Riviera...'

Both want to own the capsule now, and they try to outwit one another - until finally Carrigan's car plunges over the cliff. But she reappears as a ghost and floats into the lab

where she picks up the treasure chest and places it beside the Lazarus machine.

'My treasure!' yells Casper.

'You mean "my treasure",' says Carrigan.

Dibs comes in riding on the chair.

'Dibs, what are you doing?' asks Carrigan.

'Helping you, remember?' he says, brandishing the capsule.

As the chair docks, Kat grabs the capsule while Casper shoves Dibs into the canal. They get back on the chair and escape back to the library.

Just then the Halloween partygoers arrive at the front door. Kat lets them in and returns to the library where she hands the capsule to who she thinks is Casper.

But 'Casper' suddenly morphs back into the ghost of Carrigan, who grabs the capsule and starts to float through the wall. The capsule won't pass through and she drops it, just as the real Casper floats up through the floor to catch it!

'Let's get back to the Lazarus,' says Kat.

In the lab Dibs is trying to open the treasure chest with a crowbar. When Casper and Kat arrive on the chair he wields the crowbar like a weapon.

'That's my treasure,' says Casper.

'Forget about it, c'mon,' says Kat,

Carrigan's car teeters on the edge!

43

loading the capsule into the Lazarus. 'This is it.'

Casper opens the door, revealing Carrigan who roars into his face, blasting him backwards. 'It's my turn in the oven,' she says. 'Dibs, you worm, get this thing cooking.'

Dibs obediently drops the crowbar and crosses to the control panel. But he grabs the capsule and holds it as if he's going to break it. 'Carrigan, if there's one thing I've learned from you, it's kick 'em when they're down. And baby, you're six feet under. We're through!'

Carrigan inhales and blows Dibs up and out through a skylight with such force that the capsule hangs suspended in the air long enough for her to snatch it. She whirls on Casper and Kat. 'Any more takers?'

'No,' says Casper, 'but aren't you forgetting your unfinished business?'

'All ghosts have unfinished business,' says Kat.

'That's why we're ghosts,' confirms Casper.

'I've got my treasure,' says Carrigan. 'I've got everything. I have no "unfinished business".' Admitting this she drops the treasure chest and starts to smoke and shake. Then she disappears forever, as Kat dives to save the capsule.

The treasure chest has sprung open on the floor and Casper pulls out an old stuffed baseball. 'That's your treasure?' asks Kat.

'Are you kidding? It's autographed by Dan Brouthers of the Brooklyn Dodgers. My favourite player.'

'Casper, it's time,' says Kat.

Casper nods and makes his way to the Lazarus machine while Kat re-

The Halloween party at Whipstaff Manor

inserts the capsule in the slot. She is about to press the start button when her father appears - as a GHOST! The Ghostly Trio are right behind him.

'Dad! No!' cries Kat. 'What did you do to him?'

'Nothin',' says Stretch. 'He's just a little dead.'

Kat is devastated and begins to cry. Casper makes a quick decision. He leads Dr Harvey to the Lazarus machine. 'Come on. The living need you more than the dead.'

The Ghostly Trio swoop down. 'No you don't,' says Stretch. 'He ain't going nowhere.'

'Run along and do your chores,' says Fatso.

Casper gets really mad. 'Chores! I'm not doing any stinking chores!' His rage builds and he swells in size, getting bigger and bigger. 'And...if I want to hang out with the living, you can't stop me...you can't stop me from doing anything! Come on Doc, let's get you back on your feet again.'

He floats Dr Harvey into the Lazarus machine and then presses the start button. The Lazarus rumbles, thunders, rocks and steams. And Dr Harvey comes back to life.

Dr Harvey and Kat go down to the Halloween party, leaving Casper sitting alone with his thoughts. Amelia's ghosts appears and thanks him. 'That was a noble thing you did tonight Casper. I know Kat will never forget it. And for what you've done, I'm giving you your dream - but only until ten o'clock.'

She blows angel breath over him and he becomes a handsome boy in a pirate costume. All the girls at the party look at him as he comes downstairs and asks Kat to dance with him.

'Told you I was a good dancer,' he says as Kat's eyes widen in recognition.

Dr Harvey watches as Kat dances. Suddenly the hairs stand up on the back of his neck and Amelia steps out of the shadows. 'It's alright...' she says. 'I know you've been searching for me...but you've got to understand. You and Kat loved me so well when I was alive that I have no unfinished business. Please don't make me yours. Kat needs her father...She's growing up beautifully because of you.'

As ten o'clock approaches she eases away, touching his cheek. 'Where are you going?' he asks.

'Where I can watch over both of you...until we're together again. Goodbye James.'

Down on the dancefloor, the clock strikes ten. Casper kisses Kat gently then he disappears into thin air, causing the partygoers to scatter as they scream the biggest scream in the entire history of Friendship!

Casper the ghost continues to dance with Kat. 'Not bad for my first party,' she says.

'They'll never forget it in this town,' agrees Casper.